SOUTH AFRICAN
ANIMALS
IN THE WILD

SOUTH AFRICAN
ANIMALS
IN THE WILD

Photography: Anthony Bannister

Text: Professor John Skinner,
Director, Mammal Research Institute,
University of Pretoria

cna

Contents

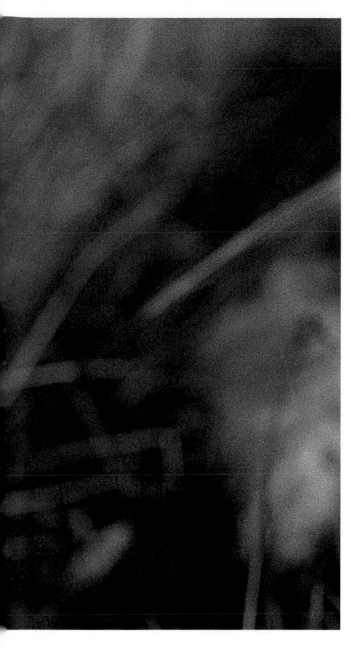

Photographer's acknowledgements

The photographs in this book reflect the generous assistance I have received from many individuals and organizations. Unfortunately the list is too long to include in full, but some of those to whom I owe special thanks are: Mercedes-Benz South Africa for their assistance with my incredible Galändewagen four-wheel drive vehicle; Frank and Hirsch Limited for expertly maintaining my 'armoury' of Nikon cameras and lenses; the Director and Staff of the National Parks Board, the four provincial Departments of Nature Conservation and the National Zoological Gardens for their assistance and for kind permission to photograph in areas under their control; Ann van Dyk of the De Wildt Cheetah Breeding Station; and Professor John Skinner and Dr Rudi van Aarde for their utmost co-operation. My gratitude also goes to the girls in my office and photographic library: Lesley Hay, Joy Trollope, Lyn Lapham, Lyn Wood and Trish Brownlow, for their hard work and the happy atmosphere they create; to my son Andrew and daughter Sue for their valued assistance on field trips; and finally, to my wife Barbara for keeping our busy home together, and for caring for David and Patrick.

ANTHONY BANNISTER

Page 1: Suricate keeping guard at a burrow entrance.
Pages 2 and 3: Red hartebeest herd.
Left: Cape clawless otter pup.
Overleaf: Springbok on the move.

Central News Agency (Pty) Ltd
CNA Building, Laub Street,
New Centre, Johannesburg 2001

Reg. No.: 01/02033/06

This book has been designed and produced for CNA by
C. Struik Publishers, Struik House, Oswald Pirow Street, Foreshore, Cape Town 8001

First published 1985
Second edition 1987

Designer: Martin Field
Setting and reproduction by Unifoto (Pty) Ltd, Cape Town
Printed and bound by Leefung-Asco Printers Ltd, Hongkong

ISBN 0 620 08402 2

Introduction

When one thinks of South Africa's wild animals it is the large mammals that spring immediately to mind, especially the so-called 'big five' – lion, elephant, hippo, rhino and the buffalo. This book is about these mammals and the many others with which South Africa is so richly endowed – the tiny elephant-shrew and hedgehog, the graceful cheetah and stealthy leopard, and antelope from the minute blue duiker to the massive eland and kudu, to name but a few.

There are in the world today about 4 500 species of mammals compared with 8 600 species of birds and 23 000 species of fishes. Of these, 338 species of mammals inhabit southern Africa and the coastal seas surrounding it. A representative selection has been chosen for this book, with photographs and text presenting interesting details about each.

While Africa is famous for its diversity of large mammalian species, the small mammals are even more diverse and unique but these are unfortunately seldom seen as most of them move around in the twilight or early morning, or under cover of darkness.

All the species in this book can be viewed in our national parks but, as will become apparent from the text, many occur only in specific regions. National parks in South Africa cover an area of 2 971 541 hectares. To this we can add the more than 70 provincial nature reserves, covering an area of 400 000 hectares, and the 300 000 hectares under the control of the Department of Environment Affairs. Many of these areas have been selected specifically to include certain habitats so that species of mammals peculiar to such areas can be conserved. It is not widely known that the South African Defence Force, which regards conservation as an important priority, controls some 450 000 hectares. This gives a total area of 5,7 million hectares, or 5,2 per cent of the surface area of the Republic of South Africa, which is devoted to conservation. Farmers, who control by far the largest area of South Africa, are also becoming increasingly conservation conscious.

Mammals have adapted structurally, physiologically and behaviourally to enable them to flourish in a wide variety of habitats. The way in which different mammals have evolved to exploit different environmental conditions makes a fascinating study. For the past two decades, scientists of the Mammal Research Institute at the University of Pretoria have played a leading role in studying the mammals of southern Africa. Much of their research has been published recently under the authorship of Dr Reay Smithers in the book *The Mammals of the Southern African Subregion*. Mammalian populations fluctuate within the limits imposed by the environment. For example, while some species will migrate, escaping to areas with more favourable conditions, yet others hibernate to achieve the same objective. The different species have developed in different ecosystems to utilize a unique niche in that system: for example carnivores eat meat, herbivores eat grass and other plants; some mammals live in burrows, others live in trees; some are diurnal, others nocturnal, and so on. There are few characteristics absolutely diagnostic of mammals but one of these is the possession of mammary glands in the female. Typical mammals have four limbs, maintain a constant body temperature, are covered with hair and give birth to live young. There are, however, exceptions to these rules – for example, the echidna and platypus, both monotremes (primitive egg-laying mammals which do not occur in South Africa), and the whales which lack hind limbs and are naked.

The mammalian body is supported by an internal skeleton consisting of a vertebral column, the skull, the ribs and the limb bones. A major characteristic of mammals is that they are endothermic. This means they can maintain their body temperature at a standard level (usually 36-38 °C) by producing heat within their bodies. This ability allows them to exploit a wide range of climatic conditions, from the polar regions to the tropics and from sandy deserts to rain forests.

The skin of mammals is also important as, in addition to hair, it contains many glands. The mammary glands are vital in that they provide nourishment for the young after birth. These glands open via nipples from which the young suckle.

The skin glands of some mammals are specialized, such as the sweat glands or scent glands which are used for advertising, either as attractants or deterrents. Some mammals have very highly developed scent glands: the hyaenas have anal glands as large as tennis balls, and the mongooses and many of their relatives have anal glands which exude quantities of fluid. Many antelope have preorbital glands (just under the eye) from which they spread a sticky substance on to grass stalks to mark their territories.

Mammal skin is usually covered by hairs. The hairs grow from living cells but are not themselves alive. The hairs serve to insulate the body, and mammals living in temperate regions tend to shed their hair in summer when it is hot, growing an undercoat for winter as the days begin to shorten. Some marine mammals, like fur seals, have thick coats but others such as whales, which have very few hairs, are insulated against the cold water by a thick layer of blubber under the skin.

Just as hairs are dead products of the skin, so too are nails, claws, hooves and horns. Horns are supported by cores of bone emanating from the skull and forming part of the skeleton. Rhinoceros horn is the exception in that it has no core of bone and is entirely a product of the skin.

Hair colours are very important for camouflage and do not necessarily represent the colour of the skin. Consider, for example, the hair pattern in the giraffe (patches) or zebra (stripes), while in both species skin pigmentation is a dark grey. Light colours help reflect the sun's rays, particularly shortwave radiation, whereas dark colours tend to absorb most of the radiation.

Endothermic animals such as mammals also control heat exchange by behavioural mechanisms. They seek shade, or lie on cold or warm surfaces. Many desert mammals are nocturnal, escaping from the high day temperatures by living in burrows. In cold conditions mammals reduce heat loss by seeking protection from the wind or by huddling together. Many species of small mammals build nests to escape from the rigours of climatic changes. Large mammals frequently change their position. For example, it has been found by researchers in Namibia that zebras and wildebeest graze with their bodies at right angles to the sun in the early morning; later in the day, when they want to lose heat, they graze with their long-axis to the sun's direct rays and thus reduce absorption.

In summary, therefore, mammals are unique when compared with other animals in that they can regulate their own body temperature, their eggs are fertilized within the female reproductive tract, and their young (except for marsupials which do not occur in South Africa) are born at an advanced stage of development. Following birth they are dependent on their mothers for a supply of milk, after which they are weaned.

Giraffe

Giraffes are by far the tallest of all living animals – most males grow to about five metres and females to about four and a half metres. Their great height makes them superbly suited to feed off the tops of trees, thereby exploiting a food source available to no other browser. Because of their specialized feeding habits, giraffes can only live where there are tallish trees and bushes. So, although they may sometimes be seen on grassy plains, they are usually just crossing from one wooded area to another. They are extremely well adapted to hot, arid conditions and are, therefore, also found along the dry watercourses of the Kaokoveld in Namibia wherever there is adequate bush.

Giraffes were once widespread throughout South Africa, but at one stage were virtually exterminated except for those in national parks and private game reserves in the eastern Transvaal lowveld. Today they are once again becoming more widely distributed. One major reason for this is that the species is regarded as a prime candidate for game farming because it fills a feeding niche not occupied by any other mammal.

Giraffes have fascinated man since ancient times; Set, the Egyptian god of evil, was depicted as having the head of a giraffe and the body of a man and, like the giraffe, was thought to live in desert regions. The first giraffe imported into Europe was brought by Julius Caesar in 46 BC to the zoo at Alexandria. With the decline of the Roman Empire, however, giraffes vanished from Europe and they were only reintroduced in 1215 when the Sultan of Egypt gave a giraffe to Frederick II, the Holy Roman Emperor, in exchange for a polar bear.

There seems to have been a co-evolution between giraffes and their favourite forage trees, the acacias *(below)*, and to a lesser extent the combretums. Although the acacias are very thorny this does not bother giraffes because they use their mobile lips and tongues to strip the plant parts they want from between the thorns. Such reliance on the acacias has its drawbacks, however, as the trees are deciduous, losing their leaves in August. For a time, despite the fact that other tree species in their habitat are well foliaged, the giraffes are vulnerable and during droughts, when the acacias are also affected,

they have been known to die in large numbers. Giraffes are a truly remarkable example of natural selection, as their long necks involve morphological adaptations such as changes in blood vessels, nerves and muscles. A frequently asked question is 'How many neck vertebrae does a giraffe have?' The answer is seven, the same as all mammals, they are just far larger. The head is so far above the heart and lungs that giraffes require a very high blood pressure and deep breathing to supply sufficient oxygen to the brain. Despite the high blood pressure in the body, however, in the brain it remains the same as that for man. This is made possible by a fine network of blood vessels, known as a rete mirabile, below the brain, which 'buffers' the blood being pumped under pressure to the head. When giraffes bend down to drink, they reduce the rush of blood to the head by spreading their legs, and the rete does the rest.

Giraffes are often seen in groups but they do not usually gather in large herds. Groups are generally made up of cows with their offspring, although bachelor and mixed herds are also found. Bull giraffes tend to move from group to group rather than form any fixed associations.

Nyala

The **nyala** belongs to a group of mainly browsing antelopes which includes the kudu *(overleaf)* and eland *(page 18)*. Males and females differ greatly in appearance, with the nyala bull *(right and below)* weighing almost twice as much as the cow. Only males carry horns and they are more spectacularly marked, having a dark brown or even black appearance.

Nyala are found only in the extreme eastern parts of South Africa, occurring in a wide variety of habitats wherever there are sufficient bushy thickets for food and cover, as well as nearby water. Although rarely seen in the Kruger National Park, except in the Pafuri area, their numbers have increased there in recent times. In most of the Natal parks, on the other hand, they are extremely plentiful and during a recent investigation into declining waterbuck numbers it was discovered that one of the reasons for this was that waterbuck were being pushed out of their prime habitat by the expanding nyala population.

Males are most commonly seen alone, but occasionally in twos or threes, invariably displaying to one another when they meet *(below)*. The sight is rather comical as each male raises his spinal crest to make himself look as impressive as possible and then slowly circles his opponent in a stiff-legged gait. Female groups *(right)* may be larger and are sometimes joined by males. Large groups of nyala have been recorded, but all these have been in open habitats where their increased numbers provide greater safety from predators.

Kudu

The **kudu** bull *(opposite)*, with its handsome spiral horns, is surely the most magnificent of the African antelopes and when groups of a dozen or more gather prior to the mid-winter breeding season they provide a spectacular sight. Unfortunately mid-winter also marks the peak of the hunting season, when this stately animal becomes a much sought-after trophy. As with nyala, kudu cows *(left and below)* differ markedly from the bulls – they are noticeably smaller and do not have horns.

Kudu are almost exclusively browsers and will eat grass only in exceptional circumstances. They are ruminants, that is they chew the cud, and they have a specially adapted stomach, divided into four sections, which enables them to digest plants. The enzymes necessary to break down the vegetable matter are not produced by the animals but are provided by micro-organisms living in the large stomach, or rumen.

Like the giraffe, kudu are vulnerable during droughts when acacias shed their leaves in response to the arid conditions, and during the ensuing food shortage kudu die in large numbers. Although starvation is the obvious reason for these deaths, other theories have been recently advanced.

Disease is often the cause of large-scale deaths among kudu and in Namibia recently many thousands died as a result of a rabies epidemic within the species. It seems likely that the rabies was transmitted from one kudu to the next via their saliva during grooming. Although in the 1950s the species was regarded as a carrier of tuberculosis and thought to infect cattle, today it is known that the kudu itself is particularly susceptible to the disease. With careful management, therefore, game farming with kudu can be very rewarding and the species is highly regarded for this purpose. As with the giraffe, the kudu's browsing habits make it ideal for farming in combination with cattle, which are primarily grazers, and provide many bushveld farmers with the opportunity to increase the productivity of their land.

Cape Eland

The **Cape eland** is the largest of the African antelope; it is even bigger than the somewhat misnamed giant eland which only occurs north of the equator. Unlike its relatives, the nyala and kudu, the eland flourishes in the more arid regions of southern Africa, where it will either browse or graze depending on the food available. It often has to travel considerable distances from one water point to the next and during these migrations it obtains enough liquid for its needs from juicy plants.

Eland are prominently depicted in Bushman rock art in southern Africa and they were prized by these people for their flesh and the fat stored in the dewlap. Because of their excellent meat and milk, eland were long thought to be ideal for domestication as they are also very resistant to disease. Many decades ago a number were even exported to Russia, where a dairy herd still exists today – eland milk is believed to have outstanding medicinal properties, but there is no proof to justify these claims.

Studies by the Mammal Research Institute in South Africa have, however, shown that the eland is not as well suited to game farming as was originally thought. It is a nomadic species and does not thrive in captivity. When confined it tends to damage trees by breaking off branches, adeptly twisting the limbs between its horns. Although the eland tames easily, the bulls are unpredictable and not to be trusted, and there are many reports of their attacking people. They are also very difficult to confine as in spite of their size eland are great jumpers and can clear a 2,5 metre fence from a standing start.

Gemsbok

The striking **gemsbok** is a gregarious oryx and may gather in herds of up to 12 individuals. Smaller groups of two or three are also common, however, and occasionally a lone male may be seen. Males and females are very similar but the females' horns are longer and more slender. The gemsbok inhabits the arid western parts of southern Africa and even thrives in the inhospitable wastelands of the central Namib Desert. To do so it has adapted superbly to dry conditions; it is able to travel great distances in search of food and can go for long periods without drinking, as succulent desert plants and early morning dew on leaves provide enough moisture for its needs.

The gemsbok's ability to conserve body fluids is remarkable. For example, its urine is very concentrated and only a small quantity is excreted at a time, while the faecal pellets are very dry. A further water-saving mechanism is the ability, during the heat of the day, to tolerate a body temperature increase of some five or six degrees above the 37 °C regarded as normal for most mammals. The gemsbok reduces the rate of heat absorption as much as possible, however, by keeping its cylindrical body angled away from the sun. Then at night, when the desert air cools sharply, this 'stored' body heat is lost through radiation and the animal's temperature returns to normal without water loss. Throughout this process, however, the gemsbok's brain has to be maintained at normal body temperature. To achieve this, blood passes through a network of capillaries in the nose where it is cooled by the evaporation of moisture as air is drawn through the nostrils. This cooled blood then moves to and surrounds the arterial network below the brain. In this way heat is exchanged with warmer blood on its way to the brain, thus cooling it.

Adult gemsbok have formidable horns and fights at water holes are common, even between females at times, when rival herds meet. It seems that the horns are little defence against predators, however, as research has shown this antelope to fall prey to spotted hyaenas in the Kalahari and the Namib, where particularly the very young and the old are this carnivore's major food source.

Roan and Sable

The **roan** *(left)* is the second largest antelope in southern Africa, only the Cape eland being bigger. Its very wide distribution notwithstanding, the roan is considered endangered in many parts, and the Kruger National Park with its population of some 340 has long been regarded as the most important conservation area for the species in southern Africa.

One of the main reasons for the plight of the roan is its particular habitat needs, for it prefers woodland in which there are open areas through which it can move, grazing taller stands of grass. It does not tolerate woodland where trees form close canopies or thickets and, for this reason, bush encroachment and over-use of grasslands by

other species has in many areas limited its recovery.

Another factor is the roan's susceptibility to disease. In the Kruger National Park, where it is particularly vulnerable to anthrax, the Park's biologists have done a superb job in developing a vaccine and inoculating the herds. During darting the antelope are marked with a dye so that the biologists can identify inoculated individuals. In 1968 sixteen roan were translocated from the Waterberg to the Percy Fyfe Nature Reserve, where they now flourish to such an extent as a breeding herd that 12 were returned recently to their original home in the Lapalala Game Reserve in the Waterberg. The stately **sable** *(above and top left)* can use its great scythe-like horns to good effect. Bulls are fiercely territorial and will set about trespassers in no uncertain terms. Under confined conditions, such

as in game parks, they are especially aggressive and evict young males from the herd when they reach 15 to 18 months. If these youngsters are unable to escape they are invariably killed.

In the mating season bulls can be seen testing cows to see whether they are on heat. They can tell this by sampling the cow's urine and then demonstrating flehmen *(above)* in which the male wrinkles up his nose following stimulation of sensory receptors in the nostrils. Sable are able to adapt better to habitat changes than roan and are less vulnerable to disease, but they are nevertheless regarded as rare animals. While a nucleus population in the Hans Merensky Nature Reserve has been used to establish new breeding herds in other Transvaal reserves, the Kruger National Park remains South Africa's major area of conservation for the sable.

Waterbuck

Waterbuck are easily identified as both the male and the female have a distinctive target-like white ring around the rump. The purpose of this marking is not clear, but could be a device to help their young follow them through thick vegetation. Only the males have horns.

Waterbuck lack the water-conserving ability of antelope inhabiting arid regions and, as their name implies, they are never found far from reedbeds, vleis, rivers and dams, or wherever else there is permanent water. Although their dependence on water limits their distribution they do thrive outside of reserves, and on many farms in the northern Transvaal waterbuck have migrated up water courses to colonize suitable areas.

These predominantly grazing antelope are gregarious, forming small herds of six to twelve led by a territorial bull. Breeding takes place throughout the year and when a calf is born it is hidden in the thick undergrowth where it will remain for the first four weeks, until it is strong enough to follow its mother.

Tsessebe and Red Hartebeest

Like roan and sable, **tsessebe** *(above and left)* were once relatively widespread in the Transvaal but were later almost exterminated through hunting and destruction of their habitat. Bush encroachment continues to threaten the species as tsessebe are very dependent on open savanna where there is a permanent water supply. Until recently they remained only in the Kruger National Park, near Klaserie in the Transvaal lowveld, and in a few scattered groups in inaccessible areas in the Waterberg. Today the outlook for tsessebe is much brighter as the Transvaal Division of Nature Conservation has had considerable success in translocating these antelope to other reserves for breeding and redistribution.

Although tsessebe usually live in small family parties – a territorial bull, his harem and their offspring – large herds do occur *(above)*, often in association with other plains animals such as Burchell's zebra. Confusion in distinguishing between tsessebe and the **red hartebeest** *(right)* is unlikely as the latter is found usually in the more arid parts of southern Africa. Red hartebeest are particularly plentiful in the Kalahari Gemsbok National Park where herds of up to 20 members are common. Hartebeest and tsessebe have an awkward rocking gait when they run, but this belies their speed and stamina for they are among the fastest of the plains antelope and can keep going at full tilt for many kilometres to escape predators.

Bontebok and Blesbok

Bontebok *(left and far left)* and **blesbok** *(below)* were long thought to be separate species, but in recent times they have been classified as subspecies of the same animal. Even this is in some doubt and a growing number of scientists regard them simply as colour variations of the same species. Certainly there is little to distinguish them physically, apart from slight differences in colour and facial markings. Both animals occur only in South Africa, but their ranges do not overlap as the bontebok is confined to a small area within the south-western Cape, while the blesbok has a wider distribution across the Cape midlands and into the Orange Free State.

In the mid-1800s, the bontebok was poised at the brink of extinction and, had it not been for the far-sightedness and timely action of a group of Bredasdorp farmers, the species would have been wiped out as was the blue antelope which once inhabited the same region. These farmers protected 27 bontebok to form a breeding population on the farm Nacht Wacht where they thrived. In 1931 the first Bontebok National Park was proclaimed and 22 antelope from the original stock were relocated there. The project was not a success, however, as the area was unsuitable – bontebok are exclusively grazing animals and short grass and adequate drinking water are essential habitat requirements. In 1960, the problem was solved when 84 bontebok were moved to the larger, better area which is the present National Park. The future of the bontebok now seems assured – numbers have increased and since 1969 surplus stock has been made available to farmers for game farming and breeding.

Blesbok, too, were hunted extensively, to the point where they were seldom seen. As with the bontebok it was the farmer who came to the rescue, conserving small herds for game farming. Blesbok are highly regarded for this purpose as they are easily confined by farm fences, and their meat is excellent.

As with bontebok rams, male blesbok are very territorial and before the autumn mating season they are a common sight as they display themselves at regular intervals across the veld to attract females. They are very reluctant to leave their posts and this contributed to their previous vulnerability as they made easy targets for hunters. Also, displaying bulls were once regarded as rejects from the herd and farmers were often unwittingly guilty of shooting their prime rams. This had serious repercussions as it created a 'vacuum' of a few weeks before they were replaced by other rams – a male blesbok needs to establish a territory before breeding. Such a shortage of breeding males, even though temporary, can be disastrous for the birth rate for once the breeding season has passed the females do not come on heat again for a full year.

Blesbok ewes lamb in November, after the first rains. This strategy is typical of antelope which have evolved in the highveld with its summer rainfall, for it ensures that lambs are born when there is plenty of green grass to nourish nursing mothers.

Some 80 per cent of breeding ewes drop their lambs within a fortnight of each other. This phenomenon occurs with many plains antelope and is an interesting survival mechanism as, at a time when lambs are very vulnerable, predators are so swamped with prey that most of the young blesbok survive.

Wildebeest

Wildebeest are often referred to as the clowns of the veld. Certainly their appearance is most comical and their head- and tail-tossing antics draw many a smile. There are two species, the **blue wildebeest** *(left and above)* which is widely distributed throughout savanna woodland habitats and the **black wildebeest** *(top)* which is far less abundant and is only found in the grasslands of the central plateau. Black wildebeest bulls, like the moulting specimen above, establish well-defined territories and make a great display when approached, snorting, threshing their blond tails and foot-stamping. Black wildebeest are predominantly grazers and tend to remain in the same area for long periods, thus maintaining grazing pressure on the land. In times past this presented no real problem, for once grazing had been exhausted and/or the water supply depleted, they would move on in search of better conditions, leaving the veld to recover. Such migrations are no longer possible because of the fenced boundaries of game reserves and farms.

Blue wildebeest are also grazers, needing frequent access to water and fresh grazing to which they will migrate over great distances. This is the antelope one associates most with vast herds trekking across the African plains. Although now far more restricted in their movements, migrating herds are still well known in East Africa and to a lesser extent in the Kalahari in Botswana.

As with blesbok and many other plains antelope, wildebeest females form into 'calving herds' and give birth within a few days of each other. In the main photograph, the female on the right has just given birth, note the afterbirth. The female on the left is typically inquisitive about a new arrival to the herd. Within a few minutes the calves are able to stand and suckle and though they are vulnerable to predation at this stage, within a day they can run fast enough to keep up with the herd.

Cape Buffalo

The large, heavily built **Cape buffalo** is regarded as one of the 'big five' by trophy hunters and photographers alike. It is a formidable, well-respected adversary and a wounded buffalo is especially dangerous. The low-slung horns, particularly those of males, are massive and develop heavy central bosses. They are not only obvious weapons of attack and defence, but probably also help the animal to maintain normal body temperature, as within the bosses there is a network of capillaries where blood can be cooled.

Buffalo usually live in very large herds *(see overleaf)* and even today these can number several thousand animals. These herds, however, are fairly loosely organ-

ized, being made up of smaller units which disperse and come together depending on the supply of food and water. Bulls often group together in bachelor herds.

Herds usually drink twice a day, in the morning and evening – the buffalo often walk into the water up to their bellies when drinking and also wallow in the muddy shallows and banks. In addition to a permanent supply of water they also need areas of veld where the grass is tall and there is plenty of shade as they spend the greater part of the day resting and do most of their grazing at night. Their mouth parts are well suited to feeding on long grass; using their tongues to pull the grass into their mouths, they bite off the stalks by moving the lower incisors against the dental pad in the upper jaw.

These large grazers can have a profound effect on grass cover if herd numbers build up excessively. For this reason the Kruger National Park authorities need to cull several thousand each year to prevent overgrazing in the fertile environment of the Park.

During the recent wet cycle in the lowveld, buffalo numbers increased considerably in all game reserves, but in the subsequent drought they suffered badly as they cannot adapt to dry conditions and find it difficult to find enough food when the grass is short. Adequate fodder is particularly important to ensure good milk production in nursing cows and the majority of births take place in January and February, following the major growth period of grass.

Like so many wild animals buffalo are troubled by skin parasites and, while wallowing helps to keep these in check, many persist, especially ticks which burrow through the buffalo's thick hide. The red-billed oxpecker (*left*) is a welcome visitor, therefore, as it scours the buffalo, pecking out the ticks which are its staple food. As many as a dozen of the birds may be seen on a beast at any one time and they serve another useful function as they will fly up calling raucously to alert the herd to any possible danger.

Impala

Impala have evolved along the moist, eastern side of Africa and are never far from permanent drinking water *(below)*. They favour acacia-mopane woodland habitats which provide them with a good supply of high-protein browse.

Male and female impala look very much alike, but the rams are easily identified by their stately lyre-shaped horns *(bottom left)* and during the rutting season are a common sight in the game parks as, with much clashing of horns *(left)*, they do battle to establish and protect their territories.

Like wildebeest, impala lambs are born within a very short period and when the ewe is ready to give birth she withdraws from the herd to find a sheltered spot *(right)*. After a few days mother and off-spring return to the herd.

Impala are prolific breeders and their large numbers make them a major food source for all the big predators.

Springbok

With ears pricked, alert to any sign of danger, the **springbok** ewe *(left)* is a lovely sight and it is appropriate that as one of South Africa's most plentiful antelope it is our national animal and the coveted emblem of our sportsmen. Springbok have evolved in the arid, western half of Africa – although they are also found on the highveld – and, like other antelope which have adapted to a drier climate, they need little drinking water. They obtain most of their liquid requirements from young succulent grasses and Karoo scrub and by grazing at night when the moisture content of vegetation is higher.

In the past century springbok were renowned for their great treks when herds of thousands upon thousands would migrate over considerable distances, moving instinctively towards areas where rain had fallen and grazing was good. Such 'tidal waves' of springbok are not known today but herds can still be impressively large as the photographs show. Normally slow moving, springbok are nevertheless extremely fleet-footed and can achieve speeds approaching 90 kilometres an hour, often leaving the ground in great leaps of up to 15 metres in length. When agitated, springbok will perform spectacular, vertical jumps known as stotting ('pronking'), when, with arched back and all fours leaving the ground at the same time, they leap as high as two metres into the air.

Springbok venison is highly regarded and is in great demand both locally and abroad. The antelope are ideally suited to game farming as they can be contained by ordinary fencing and have a high reproductive rate.

Reedbuck and Bushbuck

As their name suggests, **reedbuck** *(top right)* are found near vleis or in reedbeds where there are stands of tall grass. Because of their particular habitat needs reedbuck have a very patchy distribution in South Africa. They have also been exterminated throughout much of their range and are regarded as an endangered species in the Transvaal outside of the Kruger National Park.

Reedbuck are almost exclusively grazers and are strongly attracted to fresh sprouting grass following burning. Water is essential – reedbuck cannot survive without it and will move to new areas if pools near their feeding grounds dry up. They are shy, secretive animals which tend to feed during the evening or early morning when it is cooler, and spend much of the day resting up in some shaded spot. During dry periods, however, when food is hard to come by, they are seen more frequently during the day. When surprised they make a characteristic whistle produced by expelling air through the nostrils. They breed throughout the year, but most young are born in the summer months.

Bushbuck, like their cousins the nyala, are handsome, well-dressed creatures, but they are seldom seen for they are secretive, predominantly nocturnal animals and confine themselves to thick bush and riverine forest. Often the only hint of their presence is a characteristic warning 'bark'. Even if they are within sight they are difficult to spot, for – as the photographs *(left and bottom right)* show – bushbuck have distinctive white markings on a dark brown body which blend with the dappled light of their environment. Lambs are born throughout the year but are seen even less frequently than adults as their mothers hide them away in the dense undergrowth. Bushbuck are generally solitary but sometimes occur in pairs or in small groups.

Only the rams have horns and these they use to great effect against rival rams, often in a fight to the death, as well as against predators. If cornered, wounded rams are dangerous and fight courageously. Many stories tell of encounters where man and his dogs have been bested and sometimes even killed.

African Elephant

By any standard the **African elephant** is massive and is by far the largest and heaviest of the world's land mammals. Mature males such as the specimen opposite may reach a mass of five tons and cows not much less.

All males have tusks as do most females – the cows of the Addo National Park being the exception. Even at birth calves have a tiny pair, but these are like milk teeth in humans and when the baby elephant is about a year old they are replaced by a permanent pair which grows throughout the animal's life. The tusks are in fact large, continuously growing upper incisors, covered at an early stage of development by a cap of smooth enamel which is quickly lost. Wear of the tusks is uneven and consequently right and left tusks may differ in size.

The elephant's bulk makes heat loss difficult, especially as it lacks sweat glands. But it has evolved a unique way to cope with the problem. The elephant's ears are enormous and although they weigh only some 20 kilograms apiece, they form roughly 20 per cent of the animal's surface area. And it is these huge organs that provide the major avenue for heat loss as they are richly supplied with blood vessels and as blood passes through them at a rate of 5-12 litres a minute, it is cooled in much the same way as water passing through the radiator of a motor car. The elephant also flaps its ears to move air over them and to produce a cooling breeze over the body. Although the ears are responsible for as much as three quarters of the heat loss necessary to maintain normal body temperature, water is needed to complete the job and some 30 litres are required daily, not for drinking but solely for the elephant to spray over its body to keep cool. Elephants will drink as much as 150 litres a day if they can. Wallowing in mudholes *(overleaf)* is a favourite pastime, not only helping to cool their bodies but ridding them of parasites as well. Elephants also consume vast quantities of food – about 200 kilograms a day each – and this they get from trees and grass using their versatile trunks to pluck the vegetation and transfer it to their mouths. They are very destructive feeders, especially the bulls which will push down whole trees to reach a few juicy leaves and will strip the bark from certain species, particularly acacias, causing them to die.

A characteristic of elephants is their matriarchal society, females and their young associating in very closely knit groups. These in turn combine with other family groups to form the breeding herds. Calves may be born at any time of the year following a gestation period of 22 months.

Bulls tend to congregate in bachelor herds but these are loose associations with members tending to come and go. Very old males are usually solitary. Serious fighting can break out between males over a female on heat but usually some head pushing and tusking *(below)* is enough to settle the issue.

Elephants in southern Africa are also famous because of the last survivors of a once-viable herd occurring in the Knysna Forest. Only three elephants are left in the forest and, alas, this is not a habitat of their choice but one which they have sought as a result of persecution by man. The same fate nearly overtook the Addo elephants, but fortunately a national park was declared and a heavy-duty perimeter fence was erected to restrain them from marauding forays into neighbouring farms and suffering the same fate as the Knysna elephants which resorted to this practice.

Duiker

The minute **blue duiker** *(above and above right)* is the smallest of the South African antelope with the male and the female each weighing only about four kilograms. It occurs in Natal from the Umfolozi down the coast and in the Cape between East London and George. The somewhat limited distribution range is further restricted by the species' specialized habitat needs as it is confined to forest, thickets and dense coastal bush. The blue duiker is seldom seen as at the slightest hint of danger it darts away into the forest growth, following its regularly used paths. As a result it is frequently caught by poachers exploiting this habit. It feeds on leaves and shoots as well as fruit. Both sexes are horned. The blue duiker breeds throughout the year, giving birth to a single young at the end of each gestation period.

Though also small, the **common duiker** *(left)* is five times larger than its blue cousin. Its colour is extremely variable and although it is often referred to as the grey duiker it is in some regions distinctly reddish. Unlike the blue duiker, only the male carries horns. This species also frequents wooded areas, but the duikers' ranges do not overlap as the common species is widely distributed throughout the montane forest regions of South Africa while the blue duiker is found only along the coast.

The common duiker feeds in the early evening and at dawn, but its main period of activity can extend well after sunset. It is principally a browsing animal and rarely eats grass, but fruits and seeds of trees are included in the diet. Studies by the Mammal Research Institute have shown the antelope to be something of a problem in the pine plantations of the eastern Transvaal, as the young trees can be seriously damaged during their first year of growth as a result of duiker browsing. The common duiker has also been known to eat young birds.

Oribi and Klipspringer

The **oribi** *(above and right)* and the **klipspringer** *(opposite)* inhabit two different extremes of habitat: the former, the open grassy plains of the highveld, and the latter, stony koppies wherever these occur.

Oribi are yellowish with a rusty tinge and have a fine, silky coat which is much shorter in summer than in winter. Only male oribi have horns. Although oribi once had a wide distribution in South Africa, in many areas their existence is being threatened for two major reasons. First, large areas of their former habitat are now being used for crops or plantations of wattle, pine and eucalyptus trees. And secondly, their preference for an open habitat has made the oribi vulnerable to poachers, particularly to those using dogs. As a result their numbers have been substantially reduced in the eastern Transvaal and the eastern Cape. Their survival is presently dependent on the goodwill of farmers setting aside land for them and making sure they are protected. Oribi are most frequently seen alone, although they do occur in family groups. They are territorial, using the secretions produced by a gland below each eye to demarcate their home ranges. The size of territories varies from 30 to 60 hectares depending on the suitability of the habitat. Oribi are predominantly grazers and studies have shown that they seldom, if ever, drink water, obtaining all their moisture requirements from succulent plant parts.

They breed during the summer months and females hide their newly born offspring for up to four weeks. Lambs only join the family party after about three months.

The **klipspringer** is much the same size as the oribi and is superbly adapted to life in its rocky habitats. The coat is golden-yellow to brown, the upper parts being grizzled with black. The hairs of the klipspringer's coat are unique, being hollow, flattened and spiny, and are thought to play an important part in protecting the antelope from intense radiation both directly from the sun and indirectly from its rocky surroundings through reflection of the sun's rays. The hair is also long (in the region of 20 millimetres), and insulates the klipspringer's body from extreme temperatures. It is easily shed, possibly affording the animal some protection from predators such as the leopard. The species' most special adaptation, however, is its hooves, which are oval in shape and have long, narrow soles and blunt tips which enable the klipspringer to bounce sure-footedly from rock to rock.

In addition to secretions from glands just in front of the eyes, the klipspringer uses dung heaps to mark its territory which varies in size from 15 to 50 hectares. The male klipspringer will also make his presence known by visual displays and sometimes uses such bold behaviour to challenge predators.

Researchers have discovered that a tick which parasitizes the red rock rabbit completes its cycle on the klipspringer. To get on to its host the tick is attracted to twigs marked with secretions from the antelope's facial glands and crawls up the stems. As and when the klipspringer reaffirms its territory the tick is ready to climb on to the beast.

Klipspringers are predominantly browsers but they also eat berries, fruit, seeds and flowers. Following a gestation period of about five months, a single lamb weighing about a kilogram is born. These lambs remain hidden for the first three months of their lives.

Steenbok and Grysbok

Steenbok *(right and below)* are widely spread throughout South Africa and are second only to impala as the most numerous game species in the Kruger National Park. They are small, graceful antelope, rufous brown in colour. Only the male *(below)* has horns. Because they inhabit open country and are daytime feeders they are often seen. Steenbok are territorial and both sexes will defend their territories against intruders, a habit shared with the klipspringer. They obtain their moisture requirements from their food and are known to dig for bulbs and roots as well as for selecting succulent plant parts. A characteristic of steenbok is that before they defecate or urinate, they first clear a spot with their front hooves and then, afterwards, carefully cover the contents by scraping soil over the spot. They are particularly well adapted to a hot, arid climate and because of their small size can make use of tall grass and small shrubs to escape the heat of the day. They breed throughout the year giving birth to a single lamb.

Grysbok *(opposite)* are confined to the fynbos region of the southern Cape. Hardly anything is known about these small antelope, particularly as they are nocturnal. Although they are predominantly grazers, they also eat fruits. They also pose something of a problem for wine farmers as they are particularly fond of vine shoots.

Hippopotamus

The **hippopotamus**, among the largest of the land mammals, once occurred in rivers throughout South Africa, but the species has been hunted to the point where it now only occurs in nature reserves. It is very susceptible to heat and sunburn and in summer spends much of the day in the water, often with only its eyes, nostrils and ears above the surface, and sometimes submerging completely, staying underwater for as long as six minutes if alarmed.

Hippos do not feed in the water and at night they leave their daytime habitat to forage on land. They are grazers and, as one would assume from their size, they consume vast quantities of grass, cropping it very closely. Usually their feeding grounds are within a few kilometres of their water territories, but during droughts when they are very vulnerable to starvation they frequently have to wander great distances and have been known to trek 30 kilometres to find enough food. They are notorious for foraging crops, which provide them with a highly nutritious source of food, and are the bane of agriculturists who use the rich alluvial soils near rivers and waterways to plant their crops.

Mating takes place in water and the gestation period is about eight months. Females can conceive from the age of four years, but males develop later and only reach puberty when they are about seven years old. This enables them to remain with the family group for longer as once they start taking an interest in the females they are expelled by the herd bull.

The hippo yawn is often a sign of aggression and even a young animal *(above right)* displays a formidable array of teeth. The huge canines in the lower jaw are the largest and heaviest of their teeth, and during the last century hippos were often shot for this ivory. The canines and the incisors are useless for feeding and are used only as weapons of attack or defence. To crop grass they use the hard edges of their lips. The cheek teeth are used to grind the food which is then broken down in the multi-chambered stomach with the aid of microbes. In common with the elephant, but unlike antelopes, the hippopotamus does not chew the cud.

Zebra

Mountain zebra are restricted to mountainous areas and are divided into two subspecies, the one living in the highlands of Namibia and Angola and the other, known as the **Cape mountain zebra** *(left)*, being endemic to high altitude regions of the Cape. On the other hand, **Burchell's zebra** *(below, below left and overleaf)*, also known as plains zebra, flourish on the eastern side of Africa from Kenya to Natal. Mountain zebra are remarkably nimble and their hooves are able to grip on almost sheer rock faces. They are also better adapted to an arid environment.

In early times Cape mountain zebra occurred as far north as the Suurberg and Stormberg but by 1936 the species was almost extinct. In 1937 the Mountain Zebra National Park was proclaimed and held five stallions and one mare. By 1950 only two stallions remained and their numbers were bolstered by five stallions and six mares from an adjoining farm. This number proved sufficient to form a breeding herd and the population currently stands at 235. A further 35 Cape mountain zebra have been relocated in other sanctuaries in the province. Zebras are not territorial animals and usually form family groups comprising a stallion, his harem of mares and their offspring. Bachelor herds also form and sometimes associate with family groups where they are tolerated by the herd stallion provided the bachelor males remain submissive.

Rhinoceros

The name **rhinoceros** derives from the Greek words *rhis,* meaning nose and *keras,* meaning horn, and relates to this mammal's most obvious characteristic. The horns have no bony core such as those of antelopes, but instead consist of compacted fibres placed on the skull. The horns grow continuously but wear and tear restricts growth of the front horn to about 60 centimetres, the second horn to about 24 centimetres.

Both species, the **black** or **hook-lipped rhinoceros** *(left and opposite)* and its larger relative, the **white** or **square-lipped rhinoceros** *(above and overleaf),* were formerly widespread throughout southern Africa, but with hunting, and the increase in human settlement and resultant pressure on land, they were in danger of becoming extinct. In the Kruger National Park the last naturally occurring hook-lipped rhino was seen in 1936. Hook-lipped rhino were saved from extinction in South Africa by the proclamation of the Natal game reserves and through this protection, numbers have increased steadily to the point where they have been relocated to other sanctuaries.

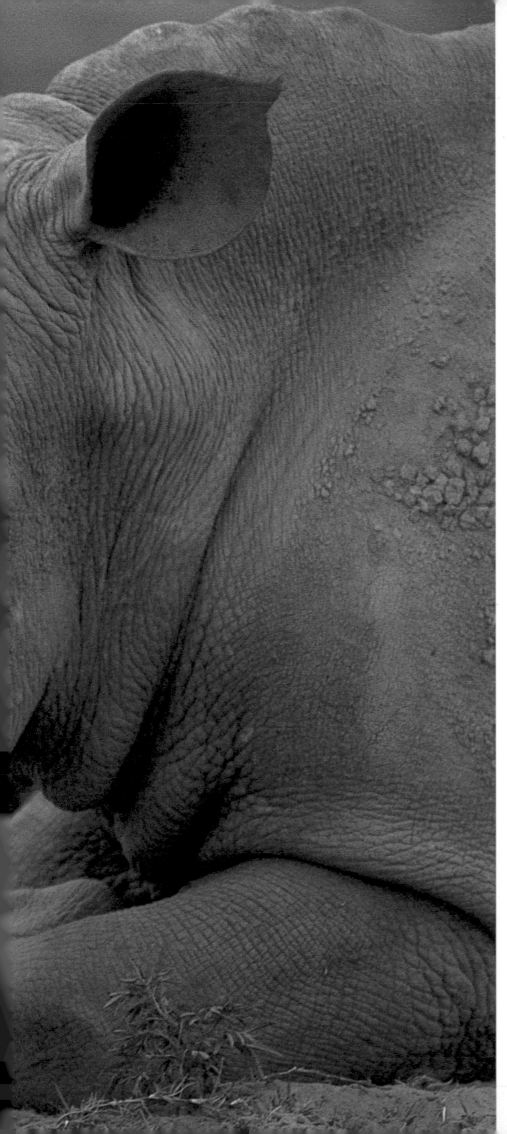

An interesting translocation was that of seven hook-lipped rhinos from Kenya to the Addo Elephant National Park in 1961.

These represent the subspecies *Diceros bicornis michaele* which are now endangered in Kenya, so the twelve existing in Addo have become very important. The hook-lipped rhinoceros is a browser and needs a good supply of fodder trees and shrubs. Climatic cycles are therefore very important in population growth. During wet cycles when the bush flourishes and there is plenty of food, rhino populations increase, but during dry cycles less food is available and populations tend to decrease. They are dependent on surface water for drinking and wallowing which helps them to keep cool and to rid themselves of parasites. Hook-lipped rhinos are solitary creatures and are well known for their aggressive attitude towards intruders and will charge at the least provocation. They have poor vision and rely mostly on sense of smell to locate an adversary. Extremely agile for their size, they can quickly change direction, even when charging at about 50 kilometres an hour.

During courtship the bulls, although not territorial, are extremely intolerant of others. Calves weigh about 40 kilograms at birth, following a gestation period of 15 months. Females with young calves are notoriously ill-tempered and should be avoided.

The case for conservation is epitomized by the saga of saving the **square-lipped rhino** *(left)* from extinction in South Africa. The species came close to being wiped out in the early years of this century, but thanks to timely action taken by the Natal Parks Board and other authorities, the saving of this rhino has become one of the most successful conservation projects in South Africa. At the turn of the century there were only about ten square-lipped rhinos in Natal and, by 1916, these had increased to about 40. By 1930 estimates were put at about 140 and by 1960 at just over 700. Since 1960 numbers in the Natal game reserves have more than doubled and nearly 300 have been relocated in other sanctuaries.

While the future of the square-lipped rhino has been ensured in South Africa, in north-eastern Africa west of the Nile River, it has suffered severely from poaching and only a few survive. The alarming decline is a result of the rapid increase in the value of rhino horns. Although thought to be popular as an aphrodisiac and for medicinal purposes, it is the use of rhino horns for making dagger handles in north Yemen which is largely responsible for the demand.

In contrast to black rhinos, the white rhinos are grazers, having a marked preference for short grass. They lack incisor teeth, using instead their sensitive movable upper lips to crop grass to within a centimetre of the ground. Surface water is important for drinking and wallowing.

Rhinos are long-lived, with hook-lipped rhinos reaching 40 years and square-lipped rhinos 45 years of age. Females first begin to breed at the age of four to five years. Males may breed at seven to eight years but social factors, such as certain bulls dominating the females in the herd, usually preclude this.

Chacma Baboon

All baboons in South Africa are **chacma baboons,** but within the species there is a confusingly wide range in colour variation, both between individual troop members and between troops. Some of these colour differences are due to sex and age; for example, old males tend to be much darker.

Troops may comprise 100 or more individuals and display a high degree of social organization. The number of dominant males in a troop varies, each has a different role to play and they are in the forefront of encounters with other troops. Certain males are responsible for activities such as sentry duty and while the rest of the troop is feeding, they will take up a vantage point so that they can warn of approaching predators. Other males will keep the young from straying while the troop is on the move. Although there are many stories of vicious inter-troop battles, this is not the norm. In three-quarters of encounters between troops recorded by scientists from the Mammal Research Institute, it was found that no fighting occurred, but that when it did, it was indeed very fierce, with even immature members participating.

Chacma baboons are frequently seen in the company of antelope or other foraging animals. Their companions benefit from the association for the baboons dislodge wild fruits which would otherwise be out of the antelopes' reach, and at the same time help to promote the safety of the grazing species by acting as look-outs.

Baboons have an extremely wide-ranging diet, including insects and a variety of vegetable matter: there are many records of their raids on mealie fields and fruit orchards, making them highly unpopular with farmers. They are also known to prey on the young of antelope such as klipspringer and steenbok, as well as farm livestock.

In keeping with the strong social behaviour of baboons, there is a close bond between the newly born and its mother. She will carry her baby about and groom it constantly for two to three months, not permitting other females to pick it up until it can walk. Young are suckled for about six months.

Vervet Monkey and Lesser Bushbaby

The **vervet monkey** *(left)* inhabits savanna woodland and is widespread throughout southern Africa. It is very gregarious, occurring in troops of up to 20. There is a 'pecking order' within troops, and during squabbles subordinate monkeys are often bitten, particularly on the base of the tail – a convenient method of recognizing low-ranking monkcys. Vervet monkeys are very vocal and will give vent to feelings of hunger, pain or alarm. The presence of young seems to strengthen bonds within a troop for females are very maternal and protective towards infants, and will even accept strange juveniles into the troop. Vervet monkeys spend much time in trees searching for food but they are equally at home foraging on the ground, if food is to be found there. Predominantly herbivorous, they include fruit, seeds, flowers, buds, leaves, bark, gum, roots and bulbs in their diet, but they also take small animals. Scientists from the Mammal Research Institute have found that young vervet monkeys learn about food from adults, whereas with chacma baboons it is often the other way around, for the young baboons are inquisitive and willing to experiment and the adults often learn from them.

The **lesser bushbaby** *(right)* is one of our most appealing small mammals. Found throughout the Transvaal, it usually occurs in some numbers in acacia woodlands as the gum exuded by acacias forms the bulk of its diet. It also feeds on insects, deftly catching them in both hands.

As its huge eyes suggest, the lesser bushbaby is a nocturnal animal and during the day families of up to seven individuals hide in disused birds' nests or in dense clumps of foliage. Research shows that the lesser bushbaby is most active in the first few hours after sunset, when it emerges from its resting place.

After mating and a gestation period of 123 days, two young are usually born, each weighing some nine grams. When setting out to forage the mother will carry her young from the nest, leave them 'parked' on a branch, and then return them to the nest before dawn. The lesser bushbaby's hands and feet are specially adapted to grip the branches along which they move, and their palms and the tip of each digit are cushioned by an enlarged, soft pad.

Warthog and Bushpig

Warthogs *(above and left)* occur in the western parts of north-eastern Transvaal, in the Cape Province along the southern border of Botswana, and in the game reserves of Natal.

The conspicuous outgrowths of skin or 'warts' from which the animal derives its name help distinguish between the sexes: the male *(above)* has two pairs, while the female has only one. The warthog's tusks are, in fact, its canine teeth which grow out sideways from the jaw.

Warthogs are animals of the day and at night will commonly lie up in disused antbear holes. They reverse into the holes so that they can face any intruder. They may use the holes also as protection from the sun on very hot days, and as maternity dens. Scientists from the Mammal Research Institute have found that within such a maternity den the female will excavate a small raised area on which to place her tiny piglets, probably to protect them in the event of flooding during thunderstorms. Warthogs are largely grazers, although they do root for rhizomes, eat wild fruits and there are records of their eating carrion.

The **bushpig** *(left above)* is widespread throughout the northern Transvaal and along the east coast as far south as George. It is associated with thick vegetation and occurs in forests, reedbeds and even where there is a heavy cover of tall grass.

When foraging, individuals within groups maintain contact by grunting softly. They eat most things and are notorious for pillaging agricultural lands at night. They can scent carrion from many kilometres away and will rapidly home in on this additional food source.

A boar marks his territory by rubbing and tusking trees to apply scent from glands which open at the base of the upper canines. Bushpigs wallow in mud to help them keep cool and as a protection against biting insects.

Lion

Lions are known to have inhabited Europe 15 000 years ago and as recently as 300 BC Aristotle mentioned lions occurring in Greece. Apart from zoos, however, they have been long gone from Europe and today lions only occur in India and Africa, although they disappeared from North Africa around 1920. They were exterminated in the Cape by the 1860s and from most of Natal shortly thereafter. Because of their habit of taking domestic livestock and their reputation as man-eaters, lions have always been in direct conflict with farmers and today are seldom found outside game reserves. Lions are, however, great wanderers, and have been known to turn up far from their expected distribution range.

Lions are known as a 'lazy' species, having short bursts of activity and long periods of relaxation. They are particularly loath to exert themselves during the heat of the day and tend to lie around in groups under shady trees. Although they are terrestrial, lions do climb and can be seen draped along the branches of trees, possibly to get the maximum benefit of breezes or to escape annoying insects.

The mane that dignifies the male of the species has a twofold function. It serves as a sexual signal, attracting females, while also making the lion appear larger and thus warning off potential rivals. It also protects the head and neck areas during fights.

Lions frequent a wide range of habitats, their most important requirements being an adequate supply of prey, and some shade in which to lie up during the heat of the day. They are well adapted to life in arid regions and occur from the Kaokoveld in Namibia as far down as the Skeleton Coast where they have recently been reported raiding seal colonies.

The social behaviour of lions has been extensively studied. They live and hunt in prides of up to 30 or more individuals and occupy home ranges which vary greatly in size, depending on prey availability. Lionesses form the nucleus of lion society, being far more active than the males in hunting, which they frequently do in pairs. Males, however, will defend the carcass against other predators; spotted hyaenas will not lightly approach a kill if a male lion is present, whereas they will pluck up courage to drive off lionesses.

While lions are catholic in their choice of prey, they tend to select larger antelope to satisfy the hunger of

the pride with fewer kills. A pride will usually kill every three or four days, depending on the prey taken and the size of the pride. Males take little part in the hunt, but are quick to feed once the kill is made, taking their fill before allowing the lionesses and cubs a look in.

Courtship in lions is an intense and fascinating process with very little aggressive behaviour occurring, unlike other mammals. The number of young born will depend on the condition of the lioness, but is usually about four. Cub mortality is invariably high and is principally caused by starvation, when the adults leave insufficient food for the young. It has been estimated that in the Kruger National Park only half the cubs born will survive, and the mortality rate is even higher in the Kalahari. Lions compensate for this high cub mortality rate as, if they are in reasonable condition, the females come on heat again soon after milk production ceases. Females may reproduce up to an age of about 15 years.

Leopard

Leopards are widespread in South Africa and in no danger of extinction. Because they prey on a wide variety of mammals from mice to animals twice their size, and because of their secretive, nocturnal habits, leopards have adapted to a wide range of habitats. Unlike other large predators, they are not only found in game parks and reserves and many still roam in the wild, on farms and near cities. They are a problem, however, as they are inveterate poachers of domestic stock and, as such, are ruthlessly hunted. In areas where food is plentiful they can rely on wild animals; for example, they are found in the Magaliesberg on the outskirts of Pretoria, where dassies are probably their main source of food. In the lowveld, impala are their most common prey.

A highly effective hunter, the leopard makes full use of bushes, trees, long grass and dappled cover, its spotted coat providing perfect camouflage as it stealthily stalks its prey, body held close to the ground. Sometimes a leopard will ambush its victim from a tree, dropping on to the unsuspecting animal's back from the vantage point of a strategically placed branch. It is an animal marvellously adapted for hunting. Close-set eyes allow binocular vision for accurate judge-

ment of distances, and its teeth are as efficient as they are impressive. The canines deliver the killing bite and tear through tough hide, while the razor-sharp molars and rasping tongue make short work of flesh.

Prey is frequently carried away or dragged up into trees to prevent it being snatched by hyaenas. In areas of Namibia where hyaenas have not occurred for decades, leopards have adapted accordingly and no longer bother to cache their prey in trees, consuming it on the ground instead.

The leopard is of average size among the big cats but it also varies in size depending on where it is found. In the Judean Desert for example, where the leopard was thought to be extinct before its rediscovery in 1972, it is small, only about half the size of the Kruger National Park leopard which, in comparison, is far larger than that found in the mountains of the western Cape.

Leopards are solitary in habit and have no particular breeding season. Litters usually consist of three cubs which remain hidden until they start to follow the mother at about two months of age. Predation on leopard cubs, particularly by other leopards and spotted hyaenas, is very common.

Small Cats

There are 28 species of small cats in the world and of these only four occur in South Africa. One of these, the **African wild cat** *(centre left)* was tamed about 3000 BC in Egypt and is thought to be the ancestor of today's domestic cat. Ironically, it is the domestic cat that presents a very real threat to the conservation of the African wild cat. Well able to survive in the wild, the domestic cat interbreeds very easily with the similarly sized African wild cat which, as a result, has disappeared in its pure genetic form from many regions. The pure form of the species is a lithe, long-legged creature, rich red behind the ears and with a black-ringed, blunt-ended tail. Like most cats it is a nocturnal hunter, with prey ranging from mice and snakes to hares and young steenbok.

The **small-spotted cat** *(bottom left)* was previously known as the black-footed cat. The current name was chosen to avoid confusion with the larger African wild cat which also has black feet. The small-spotted cat, regarded as an endangered species in South Africa, has a distribution confined to the arid central parts, particularly the Karoo. It is nocturnal and feeds on small mice, gerbils and spiders in particular. Known to be vicious and aggressive for its size, it has been suggested that the small-spotted cat may kill lambs, but this is highly improbable and arises from a mis-identification of the predator, for the offender is far more likely to be the African wild cat.

The long-legged, beautifully marked **serval** *(top left)* is one of our most attractive cats, but unfortunately it is seldom seen because of its nocturnal habits. It shelters during the day in stands of long grass, underbrush or the reedbeds frequented by its most common prey, the vlei rat and multimammate mouse. It hunts on the edge of vleis, searching among the vegetation in water up to ten centimetres deep. Water is an essential habitat requirement of the serval and its wide distribution range incorporates the wetter, eastern parts of South Africa.

On the other hand, the secretive and solitary **caracal** *(right)* can tolerate far drier conditions and is widely distributed in the central and arid parts of South Africa. This heavily built cat with its characteristic ear tufts has become a problem on farms where numbers have increased considerably with the extermination of jackals, a common predator of caracal kittens. Fast and powerful in action, the caracal is a nocturnal hunter and has been implicated in mass killings of livestock, particularly sheep and goats. It will prey on mammals up to the size of the common duiker, but its favourite prey is the rock dassie.

Cheetah

South Africa has been in the forefront of the conservation of the **cheetah,** mainly owing to efforts of the De Wildt Cheetah Breeding Station of the National Zoological Gardens, Pretoria. Many unsuccessful attempts were made to breed this species in captivity before scientists found that, in most instances, male infertility was the cause and that when fertile males were used, the problem was overcome.

During experiments in releasing captive-bred cheetah into the wild, it was found that while a certain amount of their hunting behaviour is instinctive, other behaviour is definitely acquired from their mothers. For example, the captive-bred cheetah attacked and caught small giraffes, unheard of in the case of wild cheetah. They even attempted to attack a buffalo which is way beyond their ability as, with their comparatively weak jaws and teeth, cheetah are restricted to hunting the smaller and medium-sized antelope. The cheetah is reputed to be the fastest land mammal, and when giving chase can sprint at speeds of up to 95 kilometres an hour for a distance of 100-300 metres. It is certainly superbly designed for speed, having a small head, deep chest and long legs. It uses its long, heavy tail as a rudder to balance its movements when catching prey. The cheetah differs from the other big cats in that it invariably hunts by day and seldom scavenges, preferring fresh meat.

Up to the age of about three months, cheetah cubs have a mantle of smoky grey hair concealing the spots that will later appear. This is a camouflage device designed to offer them some protection while they are still vulnerable to predation.

Honey Badger and Striped Polecat

The **honey badger** *(this page)* occurs throughout South Africa, except in desert regions. Nocturnal and usually solitary, it is aggressive if threatened and has a fearsome reputation for attacking not only man but other carnivores as well. The honey badger's black and white body is a warning coloration to other animals. If an aggressor persists in annoying it, the honey badger will exude a foul-smelling excretion from its anal glands in an attempt to drive off its attacker. With its long, knife-like front claws, thick skin and odour mechanism, it is not surprising that the honey badger

has few natural enemies. It is well known for liking the honey and larvae of wild bees but mostly feeds on reptiles and rodents which it excavates. In the Kalahari the honey badger is frequently followed closely on its foraging sorties by chanting goshawks which snap up any escaping prey. The badger can raid hives with impunity as it is protected from bee-stings by its well-padded feet and thick fur. It is also partial to geckoes and other reptiles, mice and particularly scorpions. As shown here the honey badger is an adept climber and has been seen raiding the nest of a vulture 15 metres above the ground.

The **striped polecat** *(opposite)*, like the honey badger, has conspicuous black and white colouring to warn other animals that it is best left alone. Should a possible predator not heed the warnings when the striped polecat fluffs out its long hair, curves its tail over its back and stands on its hind legs, it is liable to be sprayed with a highly persistent, unpleasant musky fluid. The striped polecat is a solitary, nocturnal animal, preying mainly on mice and insects, but also taking snakes, birds and frogs. It is a purposeful hunter and will track its prey by following a scent or by stalking.

African Civet and Small-spotted Genet

The **African civet** *(below)*, which belongs to the same family as the genet and the mongooses, is characterized by very distinctive black and white markings. Colour patterns vary considerably, with no two individuals being identical, but certain features such as the pattern combination of black, grey and white on the neck, head and ears, and the black on the lower parts of the legs, are common to all.

Civets are nocturnal, generally solitary creatures. They are confined largely to areas of the northern and eastern Transvaal where there is surface water: well-watered areas provide good cover in the form of trees and shrubs which, in turn, provide the fruit and insects important in their diet.

The **small-spotted genet** *(left)* occurs in savanna woodland throughout South Africa. It is a short-legged species with a characteristic jet black band which arises just behind the shoulders and continues down to the tail. When threatened, the genet raises this band into a high crest. While it is largely insectivorous, the small-spotted genet will also feed on birds and mice and can be a nuisance in the fowl-run. Although considered a terrestrial species, it will climb trees either voluntarily while hunting or under stress, reaching the outermost branches and hiding in thick foliage or the fork of a branch.

Opposite: Suricate (see overleaf for text).

Mongooses

Of the 31 species of mongooses, 21 occur in Africa and 11 in southern Africa. Four are dealt with here.

Suricates *(previous page)*, largely restricted to southern Africa, are certainly one of the most attractive of the mongooses. Suricates are diurnal, very sociable animals, and live in colonies. When foraging in packs they chatter constantly, and post guards to watch for birds of prey and other predators while other members search for food. They live in burrows, taking over warrens from ground squirrels or sometimes sharing the warrens with the squirrels or with the yellow mongoose. Suricates often sunbathe, sitting on earth mounds near their burrows. The mounds make good observation posts and if anything interests the suricates, they stand up on their hindlegs, using their tails for balance. They are largely insectivorous but will also take some reptiles and small birds when the occasion arises.

The **yellow mongoose** *(top right)* shows many colour variations, ranging from tawny through yellow to red depending on season or geographical distribution. Although usually seen singly, like this yellow mongoose yawning as it emerges from its burrow, it is a gregarious species and often lives in colonies of up to 20 individuals. It is a good digger and will burrow out underground tunnels and chambers, or take over those of the ground squirrel. Predominantly diurnal, its diet is much the same as that of the suricate.

The **banded mongoose** *(above)* only occurs in savanna woodland in the Transvaal and Natal. It is very gregarious, and packs of up to 75 individuals live in warrens or holes in termite mounds. Packs will attack predators and competitors, particularly when young are threatened. Like other mongooses they include eggs, insects, scorpions and reptiles in their diet and also enjoy wild fruit.

The **dwarf mongoose** *(right)* is the smallest of the South African mongooses. Very similar to their banded cousins, the dwarf mongoose lacks the stripes and at a distance appears black or very dark brown. Packs of up to 30 occur, often taking up residence in a disused termite mound.

Hyaenas

Of the four species of hyaena occurring in Africa we are fortunate in that three, the **brown hyaena** *(opposite)*, the **spotted hyaena** *(right and below)* and the aardwolf *(see page 97)*, all occur in South Africa. The brown hyaena is endemic to southern Africa, being replaced north of the Zambezi River by the striped hyaena.

The brown hyaena, a distinctive animal with a long shaggy coat and white mantle around the neck, is widely distributed throughout the arid regions of South Africa. Farmers fearing live-stock loss frequently persecute this species – unjustifiably, for this hyaena is not an adept hunt-er, and research in the Kalahari has shown that only six per cent of hunting attempts met with success. Even then, the largest animal brought down was a springhaas. The brown hyaena hunts rodents, birds, reptiles and insects, but is primarily a scavenger and with its keen sense of smell has been known to locate corpses many kilometres away. The pair shown opposite are scavenging from a gemsbok killed by lions.

Brown hyaenas are particularly well adapted to life along the cold west coast where they associate with seal colonies, preying on cubs and eating the washed-up corpses of the young seals which drown before they can swim.

Like its spotted relatives, the brown hyaena has extremely powerful jaws which cope easily with bones, hooves and horns. Both species can readily digest these items to recover the protein found in them. When meat is scarce the brown hyaena will feed on vegetable matter, especially wild melons and cucumbers which are also a source of water.

The spotted hyaena also occurs in areas inhabited by the brown hyaena but where the two compete, the brown hyaena generally will be excluded. This is because of the larger size of the spotted hyaena and the fact that it hunts in packs, whereas the brown hyaena usually forages alone.

Because they kill farm livestock, spotted hyaenas have been exterminated throughout most of their former range, and now only occur in national parks and game reserves. While brown hyaenas can also be a problem in this regard, it is usually only individual brown hyaenas that learn bad habits and so their presence passes unnoticed on many farms, whereas a pack of spotted hyaenas soon makes its presence known. In its defence, studies done by the Mammal Research Institute in the Kruger National Park have shown that spotted hyaenas, long accused of preying on wildebeest and zebra calves, took comparatively few considering the number available to them, spending instead some 40 to 50 per cent of their time scavenging, particularly from lion kills.

The spotted hyaena is a legendary animal. In the days of Aristotle it was thought to be hermaphrodite – a fallacy believed in some quarters even in recent times. This is a result of the species' very spartan social system in which the females dominate the clans, and because it is impossible to distinguish between the sexes as the external sexual organs of the females resemble those of the males. Only when females are suckling young and their teats become prominent, can they be distinguished at a distance from males.

Bat-eared Fox

The aptly-named **bat-eared fox** is widespread in the more arid regions of South Africa. During the recent three-year drought this species was found to have extended its range into areas that it had not previously inhabited. These movements are probably related not only to habitat but also to its catholic diet which allows it to adapt to a wide range of conditions. Some 90 per cent of its food consists of insects (70 per cent of these being harvester termites) and it also takes scorpions and small mice, reptiles and even wild fruit when it is available.

When foraging, bat-eared foxes appear to meander rather aimlessly but their large ears are pricked, alert to the slightest sound of moving prey. To fix the exact position of the noise, they 'point', with the ears almost touching the ground, and then begin digging using the long nails on the forefeet. The ears function not only as a 'radar' to locate prey, but also act as radiators, helping to lose body heat.

Although bat-eared foxes are largely nocturnal, they may frequently be seen during the day, particularly when it is overcast, or if food is scarce when they will be forced to spend more daylight hours searching for it.

The pair-bond is very strong and the foxes are probably monogamous. There is a definite breeding season: the arrival of the young follows the rains, a time when insect numbers are at their highest. This ensures a plentiful food supply when the young are being weaned. A litter of four cubs is usually born in a hole in the ground which the foxes may excavate themselves or which may have been vacated by antbears or springhaas. Both the male and female are attentive and protective parents. During the first excursions from the nesting burrow they will, at the first hint of danger, pick up the cubs in their mouths and carry them back to the safety of the burrow.

Cape Fox and Black-backed Jackal

The **Cape fox** *(below)*, with its soft silvery grey pelt and bushy tail, is the only true fox occurring in South Africa. This solitary, nocturnal animal inhabits the more arid regions, frequenting open country or semi-desert scrub. Prey mostly comprises a variety of small mammals, up to the size of a rabbit, and although there have been records of their attacking lambs, this occurs so seldom as to be of little importance. **Black-backed jackals** *(right)* have not been studied in any great detail in South Africa. Apart from scavenging carrion they are known to be extremely cunning predators, hunting hares, rodents, birds and sometimes newborn and small antelope. At a kill or when scavenging, the jackals observe a strict pecking order and as shown opposite, squabbles break out before they settle down to feed, with the loser adopting a submissive attitude. Although the black-backed jackal usually goes about alone or in pairs, it occasionally groups to form small family parties. They are socially very co-operative and help one another a great deal: for example, cubs from the previous two litters will assist the parents by acting as helpers with the current litter.

Wild Dogs

Wild dogs have evolved a highly specialized pack system, the chief function of which is to obtain food. Being little bigger than a jackal, a lone wild dog would lose its prey to the more powerful predators and would, in all probability, starve to death. But together, in a pack of 10 to 15 members, wild dogs form a ruthless hunting machine. They have great powers of endurance and a useful turn of speed, having been recorded at speeds of up to 66 kilometres an hour over two kilometres.

The pack system enables them to attack larger animals, such as

wildebeest and zebra, as well as waterbuck, impala and reedbuck. As their eyesight is better than their sense of smell, the dogs tend to frequent fairly open country and to hunt during the day. Prior to the hunt there is much excitement between members of the pack: twittering and squealing, they hold their tails high, rub noses and lick each other on the lips but, once on the hunt, the wild dogs are quiet. The hunt begins when the dogs course after the herd and separate their victim from the security of the group. They then proceed to chase it, sometimes for several kilometres, finally bringing it down. The way in which they do this does not endear them to the general public as the victim is literally torn apart while still alive.

Wild dog pups are well looked after by members of the pack. They guard the young at the breeding hole, and regurgitate food for them. This is in response to the ritual begging ceremony in which the young whine, nudge and bite the corners of the adults' mouths to encourage them to bring up the food. Pups first hunt with the pack when they are about two and a half months old, and at a kill they are the first to eat.

Pangolin, Antbear and Aardwolf

The **pangolin** *(above)* derives its name from the Malay *peng-goling*, meaning the roller, from its habit of curling into a ball when defending itself. An unmistakable mammal, its armour of heavy brown scales is necessary for defence as it is both toothless and slow-moving. Solitary and nocturnal, the pangolin's diet consists mainly of ants which it catches with its extraordinarily long, sticky tongue.

The **antbear** or aardvark *(opposite)* has a long, flexible snout and a sticky tongue which it uses to trap its food, predominantly ants and termites. Antbears may travel up to 16 kilometres a night searching for new termite mounds. When foraging they zigzag over the ground listening for the movement of their prey under the soil surface. Proficient diggers, they excavate extensive foraging holes and multi-chambered burrows which may later be used by other mammals, notably warthogs, porcupines and hyaenas.

The **aardwolf** *(left)* is a small hyaena weighing approximately 10 kilograms but, unlike other hyaenas, the aardwolf does not eat carrion or hunt, its prime prey being termites. Its teeth are small and peg-like and it is doubtful whether they could deal with flesh. The aardwolf digs the termites out of mounds using its powerful forefeet, and then laps up the insects with its broad, sticky tongue.

Squirrels

The **tree squirrel** *(opposite page)* is associated with open mopane and acacia woodlands, where the trees provide it with food and the abundance of tree holes it requires for nesting and breeding. During the day it can be seen foraging for flowers, fruits, seeds and leaves, ever alert for predators. If it senses danger it makes for the nesting hole, leaping from tree to tree, sometimes covering distances of over two metres in a single jump. When a female comes on heat she makes a specific call which attracts males, but it also induces other females to come on heat. As a result the births are synchronized, with many baby squirrels being born within a short time span and thus swamping potential predators.

The **ground squirrel** *(this page)* is a purely terrestrial species, commonly seen in the more arid regions of South Africa. It is gregarious and frequently occurs in association with suricates and yellow mongooses with which it occasionally shares burrow systems. They appear to cohabit peacefully but the yellow mongoose will prey on sick or injured ground squirrels.

Ground squirrels are diurnal and in hot weather are often seen with their long tails fanned over their heads as sunshades. When alarmed, the squirrels may wave their tails up and down as a visual warning to others in the group, while simultaneously calling. They have a variety of calls ranging from a growl of aggression to a high-pitched whistle or scream of alarm. Predominantly herbivorous, they will take insects when these are available.

Scrub Hare, Rock Dassie, Elephant-shrew and Springhaas

The ubiquitous **scrub hare** *(left)* occurs in such diverse habitats as the dense wattle plantations of Natal and the semi-desert conditions of southern Botswana. They are predominantly nocturnal but, in areas where they are not disturbed, they may be seen foraging at dusk. Adults vary in size, with specimens from the south-west being almost twice that of those from north-eastern areas. Scrub hares spend the daylight hours lying up in shallow depressions at the base of shrubs or other vegetation which, together with their drab coloration, provide some camouflage against predators.

Rock dassies *(opposite, top)* are widely distributed, inhabiting rocky hillsides, ravines, krantzes, or even rock piles adjacent to roadways. They are heavily preyed upon in some regions, being the prime target of leopards and caracal and a favourite prey of the black eagle. Their habit of basking in the sun renders them very vulnerable to attack, but to assist them in seeing the eagles as they stoop out of the sky, dassies have a special membranous eye shield which covers the eye when they look into the sun, thereby enabling them to see possible attackers. Numbers are strictly limited by the available shelter as once they cannot escape under rocky ledges they become even more vulnerable to predation.

The **bushveld elephant-shrew** *(opposite, bottom right)* is one of seven species of this insectivore occuring in southern Africa. Their habitat requirements range from rocky koppies to wooded areas and sand. Elephant-shrews derive their name from their trunk-like snouts which they constantly twitch up and down, sniffing the air. They show a preference for harvester termites and their tapering, pink tongues are so long that they can reach the top of their muzzles to clean the fur after a meal. Elephant-shrews are fast movers, showing a fine turn of speed when racing for cover, and are capable of great leaps, as their hind limbs are far longer than their fore limbs.

The **springhaas** *(right)* is actually misnamed as this animal is neither a hare nor even a typical rodent, and defies classification at this stage. It looks like a minikangaroo – short front legs, long powerful hind legs on which it bounds along in leaps of up to two metres, and a long black-tipped tail used for balancing. Springhaas are nocturnal, lying up during the day in the burrows which they excavate using the strong claws of the forefeet. They are mainly solitary although they may gather at good feeding grounds. They fall prey to a wide range of predators, not the least of which is man.

Porcupine and South African Hedgehog

Porcupines *(top, and bottom left)*, the largest rodents found in South Africa, have long fascinated man and many myths surround their habits and activities. For many years even some scientists believed that porcupines shot their quills at adversaries. This is a fallacy: porcupines in fact protect themselves by charging backwards to ram an adversary, leaving their 40-centimetre-long quills embedded in the enemy. This action is only taken if the aggressor does not heed the porcupine's warning of grunts, foot stamping, and raised and rattled quills. As they are nocturnal, porcupines lie up during the day either in disused antbear burrows which they modify, or in burrows they make, or in rocky caves. Once holed up they are almost impossible to remove as they erect their spines, thus anchoring themselves against the sides of the hole and at the same time presenting a sharp barrier of spines to the intruder. Porcupines are herbivores. They can be very destructive feeders and are frequently a problem in vegetable gardens as they are particularly fond of potatoes and other root crops. In the wild they debark trees, thereby killing them. The South African porcupine is known for its habit of collecting bones and it was long believed that it gnawed on these to sharpen its teeth. However, recent research at the Mammal Research Institute has shown that the porcupine may consume the bony material to rectify a calcium or phosphate deficiency in its diet.

Porcupines form a strong pair-bond, and they appear to be monogamous. One or two young are born, and are covered with soft spines which harden very quickly.

The fact that the **South African hedgehog** *(bottom right)* is now an endangered species is due in no small measure to the increased use of pesticides which poison their food of earthworms and other invertebrates.

The hedgehog occurs in many habitats, preferring grassland and woodland areas that are not too damp and that provide sufficient cover for resting up during the day under leaf litter, bushes or in holes. The resting places are changed daily, with the only semi-permanent abodes being those used for hibernation and nesting.

Covered with short, sharp spines, the hedgehog's defence against predators is to curl itself into a tight, prickly ball. However this is insufficient protection against the powerful talons and scaly feet of birds of prey such as owls.

Cape Clawless Otter and Cape Fur Seal

The **Cape clawless otter** *(left and below)* is well adapted to life on land and in water. Today it is found only in the more remote and protected areas such as along the coast and in the rivers and lakes of the Wilderness and Tsitsikamma areas, where this secretive, nocturnal animal is occasionally seen hunting crabs, octopus and slow-moving fish. Although not a marine mammal, it is sometimes seen out at sea if there are open river mouths in the vicinity. When hunting underwater the otter relies on sight and its long, sensitive whiskers to detect movement and vibrations. As its name implies, this otter has no claws on its blunt digits. Unlike other otters, its feet are only slightly webbed and its tail is the main source of propulsion when swimming.

The **Cape fur seal** *(opposite page)*, the only fur seal that breeds in this region, is widespread and inhabits coastal areas and offshore islands from Port Elizabeth to Namibia.

The young of Cape fur seals are born very seasonally in November or December. Each year the male fur seals are the first to arrive at the breeding colonies, followed some weeks later by the pregnant females. Seals mate again soon after the birth of the pups, and gestation lasts for nearly a year. During the first few days of a pup's life the maternal bond is strong, but the mother spends increasingly more time away from her pup, which joins a nursery group. Females often carry the pups in the manner shown opposite. New-born pups are vulnerable to predation both by jackals and brown hyaenas at seal colonies along the west coast. They are also the subject of much controversy as they are clubbed to death by man for their pelts. It is ironic, however, that had man not regarded this pelt production as a renewable resource, there is little doubt that he would have exterminated fur seals a long time ago.

Dolphins

Dolphins and whales belong to a group
called the cetaceans and are among the
most highly modified and specialized of all
the mammals. While they are totally aqua-
tic and never come ashore, they retain the
attributes of mammals, such as breathing
air and suckling their young. They lack
hair but are insulated against heat loss
while swimming in cold water by a thick
layer of blubber under the skin.

Twelve dolphin species occur along the
South African coast, two of the best known
being the bottlenose and dusky dolphins.
The bottlenose dolphin is the most
common in our coastal waters and is the
species popularly kept in oceanaria, as its
apparent capacity to learn and its tract-
ability in captivity make it the ideal candidate. The widespread distribution of bottlenose dolphins is mainly a result of their
catholic diet of small fish and squid. When
feeding, schools of up to 200 individuals
will form a line and drive the fish before
them in a well-organized capture
technique.

Like all whales, these dolphins have a
wide vocal range, from distress calls and
whistles to squeaks, grunts and claps.
They also echolocate: by rapidly emitting
a number of high-pitched squeaks
through the blowhole they can determine
the position of an object. The 'echoes'
bounce off the object and the reflected
soundwaves are received by canals in the
lower jaw which are connected to the ear.
The progress of a school of bottlenose
dolphins is marked by their exuberant
activity as individuals leap out of the water
or surf close to the shoreline.

Dusky dolphins, so-called because of their
colouring of deep grey backs, light grey
sides and white bellies, are also gregarious. They have strong social bonds and,
should a member of the herd be wounded
or ill, others will attempt to help by pushing it to the surface to allow it to breathe.
It is believed that in winter dusky dolphins
migrate from the cold south to the warmer
waters around South Africa, returning to
the cooler waters in summer.

Whales

In recent years the conservation of whales has captured man's imagination to a greater extent than that of any other species. Having exploited them for centuries – some species virtually to the point of extinction – man is, at last, turning to conserving all whales.

The right whales found along South Africa's coastline were given that name by early whalers because they were the 'right' whales to kill – being relatively slow swimmers they were easy to harpoon, and because of their abundant blubber, they seldom sank after being killed. Right whales were hunted not only for their oil but also for their baleen which was used during the last century to make the 'whalebone' stays of women's corsets. Instead of teeth, the so-called baleen whales have as many as 400 sheets of bone-like baleen which grow down from the roof of their mouths. When feeding, they open their strongly curved jaws and draw in enormous quantities of seawater containing squid, crustaceans, fish and krill (protein-rich shrimp-like creatures). The whales then close their lips and raise the floor of their mouths, expelling the water through the sieve-like baleen plates but retaining the food which is then swallowed whole.

Right whales have an extensive vocal repertoire. One of these calls, a low-frequency moan, travels far underwater and enables the whales to communicate over great distances. Two species of right whale frequent our waters, the rare pygmy right whale which reaches a length of about six metres, and the **southern right whale** *(below and opposite)* which achieves a length of about 18 metres.

Southern right whales were saved from extinction by being afforded universal protection in 1935. Regular aerial surveys conducted since 1962 have shown that their numbers have increased by six to seven per cent as a result of this protection and in the 1984 census no fewer than 270 whales were counted between Cape Town and Port Elizabeth. Sixty-four of these were calves.

This species is now the most common whale along our coast and is particularly noticeable when the females come in to calve *(see mother and young opposite)* in the early summer, using bays from Cape Town to Port Elizabeth. They are also frequently seen 'breaching' as shown below, when they leave the water in spectacular backward leaps, falling back into the water with a thunderous crash. The gestation period in these whales is about a year and although the calves normally have the same coloration as the adults, there have been instances of white calves recorded along our coasts.

Southern right whales have a unique feature in the wart-like protrusions situated on the front of the head before the blowhole. These callosities, clearly visible as white patches on the whales shown here, are composed of heavily cornified skin and are infested with colonies of barnacles, parasitic worms and lice. Scientists use the callosities to identify individual whales.

Common name	Scientific name	Average weight of adult male	Diet	Habits	Main feeding time	Gestation	Number of young at birth
Gemsbok (page 20)	*Oryx gazella*	240 kg	herbivorous grazer	herds	day	9 months	single calf
Genet, small-spotted (page 84)	*Genetta genetta*	2 kg	carnivorous	solitary	night	2½ months	2-4 young
Giraffe (page 10)	*Giraffa camelopardalis*	1 200 kg	herbivorous browser	herds	day	15 months	single calf
Grysbok, Cape (page 50)	*Raphicerus melanotis*	10 kg	herbivorous mainly grazer	solitary or pairs	night	6 months	single lamb
Hare, scrub (page 100)	*Lepus saxatilis*	2,5 kg	herbivorous	solitary	night	40 days	1-2 leverets
Hartebeest, red (page 27)	*Alcelaphus buselaphus*	150 kg	herbivorous grazer	herds	day	8 months	single calf
Hedgehog, South African (page 102)	*Erinaceus frontalis*	350 g	omnivorous mainly insectivorous	solitary	night	1 month	1-9 young
Hippopotamus (page 52)	*Hippopotamus amphibius*	1 500 kg	herbivorous grazer	herds	night	8 months	single calf
Hyaena, brown (page 88)	*Hyaena brunnea*	45 kg	carnivorous	clans solitary feeder	night	3 months	1-5 cubs
spotted (page 88)	*Crocuta crocuta*	60 kg	carnivorous	clans	night	3½ months	1-2 cubs
Impala (page 37)	*Aepyceros melampus*	50 kg	herbivorous grazer/browser	herds	day	6½ months	single lamb
Jackal, black-backed (page 92)	*Canis mesomelas*	8 kg	mainly carnivorous	solitary or pairs	day/night	2 months	4 pups
Klipspringer (page 49)	*Oreotragus oreotragus*	10 kg	herbivorous browser	solitary or pairs	dawn/dusk	5 months	single lamb
Kudu (page 17)	*Tragelaphus strepsiceros*	230 kg	herbivorous browser	herds	day	7 months	single calf
Leopard (page 74)	*Panthera pardus*	60 kg	carnivorous	solitary	night	3½ months	2-3 cubs
Lion (page 69)	*Panthera leo*	240 kg	carnivorous	prides	dusk/night/dawn	3½ months	1-4 cubs
Mongoose, banded (page 86)	*Mungos mungo*	1,3 kg	omnivorous	troops	day	2 months	2-8 young
dwarf (page 86)	*Helogale parvula*	270 g	carnivorous (mainly insects)	troops	day	2 months	2-4 young
yellow (page 86)	*Cynictis penicillata*	700 g	carnivorous	colonies	day	unknown	2-5 young
Monkey, vervet (page 65)	*Cercopithecus pygerythrus*	5,5 kg	omnivorous mainly herbivorous	troops	day	7 months	single infant
Nyala (page 14)	*Tragelaphus angasii*	108 kg	herbivorous mainly browser	herds	day	7 months	single calf
Oribi (page 48)	*Ourebia ourebi*	14 kg	herbivorous mainly grazer	solitary/pairs	day	7 months	single lamb
Otter, Cape clawless (page 104)	*Aonyx capensis*	13 kg	carnivorous	solitary/pairs	dawn/dusk	unknown	1-2 young
Pangolin (page 97)	*Manis temminckii*	7 kg	ants and termites	solitary	night	unknown	single young

Common name	Scientific name	Average weight of adult male	Diet	Habits	Main feeding time	Gestation	Number of young at birth
Polecat, striped (page 83)	*Ictonyx striatus*	1 kg	carnivorous	solitary	night	1½ months	1-3 young
Porcupine (page 102)	*Hystrix africaeaustralis*	17 kg	herbivorous	solitary	night	3 months	1-2 young
Reedbuck (page 40)	*Redunca arundinum*	80 kg	herbivorous grazer	small herds	dawn/dusk/night	8 months	single calf
Rhinoceros, black (page 59) **(hook-lipped)**	*Diceros bicornis*	850 kg	herbivorous browser	solitary	day/night	15 months	single calf
white (page 61) **(square-lipped)**	*Ceratotherium simum*	2 100 kg	herbivorous grazer	small groups	day/night	16 months	single calf
Roan (page 22)	*Hippotragus equinus*	270 kg	herbivorous grazer	herds	day	9 months	single calf
Sable (page 22)	*Hippotragus niger*	230 kg	herbivorous mainly grazer	herds	day	8 months	single calf
Seal, Cape fur (page 104)	*Arctocephalus pusillus*	190 kg	carnivorous	colonies	day/night	12 months	single pup
Serval (page 78)	*Felis serval*	11 kg	carnivorous	solitary	night	2½ months	1-3 young
Springbok (page 39)	*Antidorcas marsupialis*	41 kg	herbivorous grazer/browser	herds	day	5½ months	single lamb
Springhaas (page 100)	*Pedetes capensis*	3 kg	herbivorous	solitary	night	2½ months	single young
Squirrel, ground (page 98)	*Xerus inauris*	600 g	herbivorous	colonies	day	1½ months	1-3 young
tree (page 98)	*Paraxerus cepapi*	200 g	herbivorous/omnivorous	pairs/small groups	day	2 months	1-3 young
Steenbok (page 50)	*Raphicerus campestris*	11 kg	herbivorous browser/grazer	solitary	dawn/dusk	5½ months	single lamb
Suricate (page 86)	*Suricata suricatta*	730 g	carnivorous (mostly insects)	colonies	day	2½ months	2-5 young
Tsessebe (page 27)	*Damaliscus lunatus*	140 kg	herbivorous grazer	herds	day	8 months	single calf
Warthog (page 67)	*Phacochoerus aethiopicus*	80 kg	herbivorous	family groups	day	5½ months	1-5 young
Waterbuck (page 24)	*Kobus ellipsiprymnus*	260 kg	herbivorous mainly grazer	herds	day	9 months	single calf
Wildebeest, black (page 31)	*Connochaetes gnou*	180 kg	herbivorous grazer	herds	day	8½ months	single calf
blue (page 31)	*Connochaetes taurinus*	250 kg	herbivorous grazer	herds	day	8½ months	single calf
Whale, southern right (page 108)	*Balaena glacialis*	70 000 kg	small crustaceans	solitary/pairs	day/night	11-12 months	single calf
Zebra, Burchell's (page 55)	*Equus burchelli*	320 kg	herbivorous grazer	herds	day	12 months	single foal
Cape mountain (page 55)	*Equus zebra zebra*	250 kg	herbivorous grazer	herds	day	12 months	single foal